ART AND NATURE
An Intimate Close-up

THE LANGUAGE
OF ROCKS

FRITZ BERCKHEMER

Translated from the German by
ELEANOR S. SALMON
Department of Micropaleontology
American Museum of Natural History

FREDERICK UNGAR PUBLISHING CO.
NEW YORK

Translated from

DIE SPRACHE DER STEINE

Original edition published by

Verlag Die Schönen Bücher · Dr. Wolf Strache, Stuttgart

All Rights Reserved

Library of Congress Catalog Card Number 57-7665

Printed in Western Germany

INTRODUCTION

Evidence of living creatures of the past, which are embedded as "fossils" in rock, is one of the most obvious expressions of the "language of rocks." The ancient Greeks were already well on the road to understanding that language. They concluded, from the occurrence of sea shells in the interior of land, that the sea must at one time have spread over the area. Later, Leonardo da Vinci entered in his notebooks some quite correct observations on the nature of "petrifactions"; yet these ideas spread no further. On the contrary, during the Middle Ages and later, the most incredible misinterpretations of fossils were current, and even today great ignorance is often displayed in this field.

But the rigid masks of fossils were once filled with pulsating life, and the course of life during millions of years of earth history is depicted by them. With their well-ordered sequence in beds of rock that were deposited one after the other in time, they demonstrate an upward advance to ever more complex stages that cannot be ignored. In the plant kingdom, land plants first appeared after a long period of exclusively marine vegetation. From these early land plants, the fernlike plants, the conifers and their relatives, and finally the flowering plants were derived one after the other. The evolution of animals bears a close reciprocal relationship to that of plants. The origin of the phyla of lower animals is lost in the dimness of ancient time, but the chronological sequence of the appearance of the first fishes, the first amphibia and reptiles, the birds and mammals, and finally man is well established.

Recent studies based on the rate of decomposition of uranium minerals have now made it possible to estimate the actual length of time that has elapsed since the deposition of any particular rock formation. But by this means we also possess a scale for determining the age of fossils contained in rock deposits, and we are obtaining an idea of the immense periods of time throughout which life has been progressing.

F. Berckhemer

THE "GEOLOGIC CLOCK"

The basic elements in the representation of earth history are the geologic "systems." These are understood to mean extensive sequences of rock formations which are recognizable by their fossil content as belonging together. Since superposition of the beds in space (in undisturbed deposits) implies succession in time, the subdivision into systems can also be used as subdivisions of time. We speak, for example, both of the rocks of the Jurassic system, and of the Jurassic as the time interval during which these beds were laid down.

The minimum age of the earth's crust must be assumed to be approximately two billion years. We have rather accurate knowledge of only the last quarter of this time. In our diagram, these two billion years have been represented, for purposes of comparison, around the periphery of a circle. The figures given in the diagram represent average values for the time that has elapsed since the beginning of the system in question; they were derived by the uranium-lead method, taking into consideration the thickness of the rocks actually deposited.

The varying degrees of expansion of the different animal and plant groups are indicated in a rough schematic manner (plants are shown by cross-hatching, animals by diagonal bars and dots). Probable derivations and relationships are indicated by broken lines.

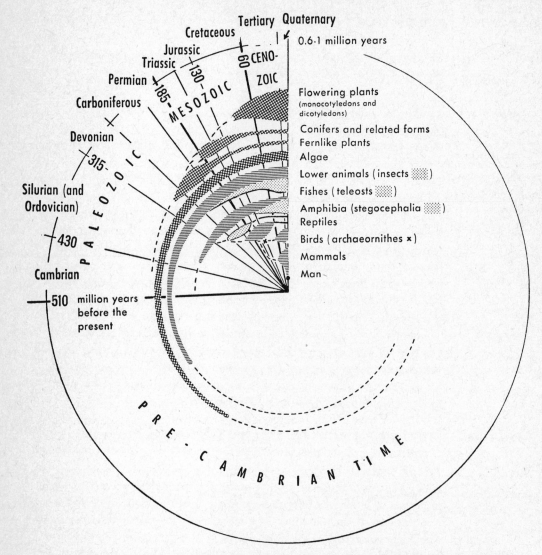

In general, the NAMES of the systems have been retained in the form in which they were first introduced to science (see the years given). They are internationally valid. Some of them were selected on the basis of the localities where they occur typically, others on the basis of a conspicuous kind of rock or an old classification.

Cambrian, named from Cambria, the Latin name for northern Wales, in the British Isles (1836).

Silurian, from the Celtic tribe of Silures, who once lived in southern Wales (1835). ("Silurian" here includes the Ordovician system, which is the modern term for the "Lower Silurian" of older geologic literature.)

Devonian, named for the county of Devonshire in England (1839).

Carboniferous (from carbo = coal), because of the coal beds that characterize it (1808). (In America the "Carboniferous" is divided into two systems, the Mississippian (Lower Carboniferous) and the Pennsylvanian (Upper Carboniferous).)

Permian, named for the former Government of Perm, on the western slopes of the Urals (1841).

Triassic, so-called because of its threefold division into the Bunter, Muschelkalk and Keuper in Württemberg (1834).

Jurassic, first studied in the Jura Mountains of Switzerland (1795). The subdivisions Lias, Dogger and Malm are derived from English place names.

Cretaceous, from the white chalk (1822). However, this system also includes sandstones, clays and marls.

Tertiary, from the "montes tertiarii," an old Italian subdivision of geologic time (1759). ("Tertiary" and "Quaternary" are remnants of an older classification in which the Paleozoic was called the Primary, and the Mesozoic the Secondary.)

Quaternary, the "fourth" division, subdivided from the Tertiary at a later date (1829). It is further subdivided into the Pleistocene or Ice Age (formerly called the Diluvium because the glacial drift was believed to be debris left by the Biblical Flood), and the Recent, or Holocene (post-glacial time, formerly called the Alluvium, meaning detritus deposited during modern times by running water).

EXPLANATORY NOTES

The plates are arranged in order of the geologic age of the specimens (see the Table of Contents on page 23).

PAGE **25** TRILOBITES ("Three-lobed Animals")
(*Ellipsocephalus Hoffi*)
Middle Cambrian. Locality: Jinetz, Czechoslovakia. Size of the rock specimen: 6.5 × 8 cm. (2.5 × 3.1 inches)

Trilobites are among the most important fossils of the Paleozoic. They are represented by a great variety of forms, which follow one another in strict chronological sequence, so that they are very valuable as marker fossils, especially for the earlier portions of this major division of time, which comprised about 350 million years. Their name is well chosen, because these animals exhibit a three-fold division in longitudinal as well as in transverse extension. After the smooth cephalon (head), there follows the thorax, composed of numerous movable segments lying next to each other. At the posterior end there is a rigid tailpiece (pygidium). The entire body is also divided into three parts by longitudinal furrows. On the left side of the plate, one of these animals can be seen in a bending attitude, as if it were just about to burrow into the mud of the sea bottom. The absence of eyes in trilobites suggests that their mode of living was largely burrowing in the mud.

PAGE **27** SHED CARAPACES OF TRILOBITES (*Dalmanitina socialis*)
Ordovician. Locality: Wesela, near Prague, Czechoslovakia. Size of the slab: 15 × 24 cm. (5.9 × 9.4 inches)

Along the seashore we often find parts of empty carapaces of the common crab. It is necessary for these animals to cast off their rigid external coverings from time to time, as the carapace repeatedly becomes too small for the animal in the course of its growth. The same process must have occurred in the trilobites of the Paleozoic. The object shown in our plate may be an agglomeration of such moulting relics washed together; we see a confused mass of heads, thoraxes and pygidia of the trilobite genus *Dalmanitina*. The species *Dalmanitina socialis* is characterized by having a distinct longitudinal impression on the "bald" area at the front, and several cross-folds on the glabella. An "eye-tubercle" is elevated above the surface of the "cheeks" on each side. All of these features are indicated merely by external and internal impressions of the carapace fragments in the rock; the thin carapace, probably composed of a substance similar to that in modern crab shells, has disappeared as a result of solution in the sandstone.

PAGE **29**   EURYPTERID ("Spiny-tailed Paddle-footed Animal")
(Eurypterus lacustris)
Silurian. Locality: Vicinity of Buffalo. New York. Natural size

The dense cement-rock in which the fossil is embedded has preserved in this case not only the impression, but also parts of the actual carapace. This is a flattened, distinctly segmented form, which lived on the bottoms of water bodies, perhaps in the transitional zone between fresh and salt water. Apparently *Eurypterus* used its tail spine to push its body along on the bottom. Anteriorly, the animal possessed six pairs of legs, of which only the last large paddle-shaped pair is visible here; they may have been used as paddles or even for digging in the mud. Just as in the case of the trilobites, these spiny-tailed animals did not survive the Paleozoic. The two groups are independent, extinct branches from the main stock of the segmented animals, or Arthropoda.

PAGE **31**   UNCOILED NAUTILOID CEPHALOPOD
(Orthoceracone or "Straight Horn") *(Orthoceras)*
Longitudinal section
Silurian. Czechoslovakia. Length: 15 cm. (5.9 inches)

Nautilus, which represents the last descendant of a group of animals that was profusely developed and widespread in the past, lives in the Indian Ocean. In its spirally coiled shell, the animal itself occupies only the most anterior portion; the rest of the shell is divided into a series of gas-filled "air-chambers" by partitions (septa); the chambers are connected with each other and with the end of the animal's body by a fleshy cord (siphuncle). This air-chamber mechanism makes it possible for the *Nautilus* to swim. Exactly the same shell structure is shown by the orthoceran illustrated here, which must therefore be regarded as an animal related to the *Nautilus.* The initial end of the shell, and the end with the living-chamber for the animal, are missing in this orthoceran, which is shown freed from the rock and sectioned longitudinally. However, the air chambers, subsequently filled with calcite crystals, with their septa curved in the form of a watch-glass, and the connecting cord (siphuncle) passing through them, are clearly visible.

PAGE **33**   BRACHIOPOD ("Arm-footed Animal") *(Spirifer macropterus)*
Lower Devonian (Spirifer sandstone). Locality: Hessen, Germany. Size of the rock fragment: 6 × 9 cm. (2.3 × 3.5 inches)
These Spirifers lie in the rock like a pair of swallows flying through the air. These are impressions of the shells of brachiopods ("arm-footed animals"). This group of animals, related to the worms, has very little

6

importance today, but many thousand species are known from the Mesozoic and Paleozoic, and countless specimens of their shells have accumulated in the rocks. In the Paleozoic especially, they consistently out-
numbered the true pelecypods (bivalve mollusks) and the snails. In spite
of their name, these "arm-footed animals" do not posses organs for
grasping or for locomotion. They are attached by means of a pedicle, or
lie free on the sea bottom. The name is based on a former misconcep-
tion of the calcareous supports extending out like arms inside the shell,
which in living forms are provided with a fringe for the absorption of
oxygen, and bear fine cilia, which aid in the capture of food by means
of their vibratory movements.

PAGE 35   STARFISH (Shield-shaped Sea-star) *(Aspidosoma tischbeinianum)*
Hunsrück shale of the Lower Devonian. Locality: Bundenbach, Rhineland,
western Germany. Size of the fossil: About 5 cm. (1.9 inches)

Storms stirred up the black mud bottom of the shallow zones of the sea,
and set free toxic products of decomposition. As a result, the starfish
shown in the plate, and many other animals, were killed. Currents in
the water turned the bodies over, and before decay could set in, the
underlying mud spread over them in a protective layer. Perhaps the
story of this animal can be interpreted in this way. That this fossil and
many others can be extracted from the Bundenbach shales so beautifully
in all their details is a result of the fact that their hard parts have been
replaced by pyrite, from which the softer shale matrix can be removed
with a needle and scraper.

PAGE 37   CRINOID ("Spiny Sea Lily") *(Agriocrinus frechi)*
Hunsrück shale, Lower Devonian. Locality: Bundenbach, Rhineland, western
Germany. Length of the calyx: About 7 cm. (2.7 inches)

In poetic comparison, these flower-like forms were once called "lilies of
the sea," and the name has been retained until the present time, although
it was long ago demonstrated that they are animals belonging to the
phylum Echinodermata ("spiny-skinned animals"), to which the starfish
and the sea urchins also belong. The differentiating characteristic of the
crinoids is their "stem," with which they can anchor themselves to the
sea bottom or to any fixed object. Ingestion of food is accomplished by
the ciliary motion of the numerous armlike appendages, as we know
from the crinoids living today. In addition to the ciliate appendages,
there are also spines on the "arms" of these crinoids of the Devonian
sea, which may have served for the purpose of warding off enemies.

PAGE 39   POLYGONAL CORAL *(Cyathophyllum hexagonum)*
Middle Devonian. Locality: Gerolstein, in the Eifel Mountains,
western Germany. Heigth of the specimen: 26 cm. (10.1 inches)

The corals of the Paleozoic lived primarily as individual corals, but they
also occur in massive colonies. An example of this is the polygonal

coral shown in the plate, whose calices are so closely appressed to each other that the rounded outline of the individual coral has become polygonal. As a colony they were better able to withstand water currents and heavy surf, and we can conclude from the occurrence of such forms that the water was relatively shallow. Only the calcareous support has been preserved. The fleshy polyps once projected above it and let their arms (tentacles) wave back and forth in the water in search of food. Many other species of corals and many forms of extinct coral-like animals lived together in a reef-like association. Crinoids and countless brachiopods were attached among them. Cephalopods related to *Nautilus*, as well as armored fish, swam about, and trilobites cleared away the refuse of the sea.

PAGE **41** PLACODERM (Armored Fish) *(Bothriolepis canadensis)*
Upper Devonian. Canada. Length 15.5 cm. (6.0 inches)

A placoderm from the Devonian is shown here. We see the well-preserved platy covering of the underside of the animal, in the form of a mass of bones, ornamented with a reticulated pattern of small grooves. Three "mouth plates" lie at the anterior end. Two "arms," also armored, are articulated at the shoulder areas; they were used for control of direction in locomotion, and also perhaps as devices to frighten off enemies. There must also have been a tail section attached, which was only loosely plated or not at all. On the upper side, the eyes lay close together near the middle of the head, so that the animal could only look upward and was therefore a bottom-living form. Although all the phyla of lower animals (invertebrates) were already represented in the Cambrian, and their origin is lost to us in the dark shadows of pre-Cambrian time, we can follow the appearances of the higher stages of life within the span of earth history that is accessible to us. The oldest fossil fish so far known at all are from the Silurian.

PAGE **43** LEPIDODENDRON ("Scale Tree") *(Lepidodendron)*
Carboniferous. Locality: Nürschan, Czechoslovakia. Natural size

A large part of our coal is composed of Lepidodendrons and Sigillarias, which formed extensive stands in the swamp forests of the Carboniferous period, and grew up to trees of considerable height. The fossil *Lepidodendron* shown in the plate lies compressed as a black carbonaceous mass in a gray argillaceous rock. The small needle-shaped leaves are present only on the younger branches. The older branches are covered with spirally arranged leaf-scars, which resemble fish scales in form and gave rise to the name. The Lepidodendrons and Sigillarias are spore-bearing plants like the ferns, which were also common during the Carboniferous. Ancestral forms are known as early as the Upper Devonian, but the principal development occurred in the Carboniferous.

8

PAGE **45**   FRAGMENT OF THE TRUNK OF A SIGILLARIA
("Signet Tree") *(Sigillaria,* subgroup *Favularia* = "Honeycomb Tree")

Carboniferous. Locality: Essen, Germany. Length of the specimen: 20 cm. (7.8 inches)

This piece of the petrified trunk of a *Sigillaria* shows principally the impression of the inner surface of the outer bark. The latter itself is also present in places, as a carbonaceous layer overlying the impression (for example, in the lower left); its surface is divided into hexagonal fields which interlock like a honeycomb, and represent the places of attachment of leaves that have fallen off. On the internal impression, however, the leaf-scars appear as beautiful pitted nodules arranged one after the other with amazing regularity like pearls on a string. We must suppose that after the tree died the perishable inner portions rotted away, and that mud, which was washed in by the water and later hardened into rock, filled the hollow space. The Sigillarias were branched, at the most, once or twice at the top. At the very top there was a crown of long narrow leaves. In the beds underlying the coal seams, the flat, outspread roots are preserved in great numbers; these roots enabled the Lepidodendrons and Sigillarias to stand in the marshy ground.

PAGE **47**   CALLIPTERIS CONFERTA ("Beautiful Fern")

Lower Permian (Rothliegendes). Locality: Lebach, Palatinate, Rhineland, western Germany. Size of the slab: 8 × 10 cm. (3.1 × 3.9 inches)

The specimen shown in our plate was not prepared or treated in any way; this fern, about 200 million years old, comes to us completely preserved by natural means. The degree of perfection of the state of preservation is not impaired by the length of time elapsed. The important factors are favorable conditions at the time when the organic remains were embedded, which must prevent decay by excluding atmospheric oxygen. The ferns developed into numerous and luxuriant forms during the Paleozoic. One group even anticipated the production of seeds, as in the later higher plants; *Callipteris* also belongs to this group.

PAGE **49**   SKULL OF A STEGOCEPHALIAN (a Primitive Amphibian)
(Archegosaurus decheni)

Lower Permian. Locality: Lebach, Palatinate, Rhineland, western Germany. Length of the skull: 15 cm. (5.9 inches)

By a fortunate blow of the hammer, the skull of an *Archegosaurus* has here been brought to light out of a tuber-like stony covering. We see the impression of the roof of the skull, with the large eye sockets and the reticulate surface sculpture of the parietal bones. To the right of it lies one half of the lower jaw that belonged to this skull, with the teeth preserved in the anterior portion. With the stegocephalians, the step from fish to land-living tetrapods was taken during the Devonian period.

10

PAGE **57**   COILED CERATITE CEPHALOPOD ("Serrated Horn")
(Ceratites)

Middle Triassic (Muschelkalk). Locality: Meimsheim, Württemberg, Germany.
Diameter: 14 cm. (5.5 inches)

The ceratite is the guide fossil to the German Muschelkalk. As early as
the Paleozoic, coiled forms related to *Nautilus* were developed, in which
the attachment of the septa of the "air chambers" to the inner surface
of the shell followed an alternately backward and forward course. In the
ceratites of the Muschelkalk, a fine serration was added on the back-
wardly-directed curves (called "lobes") of these lines of attachment,
which in technical terms are called "suture lines." The suture lines
stand out so clearly in the Muschelkalk ceratites because the outer wall
of the shell has usually been removed by natural solution; only a steinkern, or internal mold, remains. The ceratite steinkern illustrated in
the plate also shows the filling of part of the living chamber of the animal.

PAGE **59**   FROND OF A CYCADACEOUS PLANT *(Pterophyllum)*
Upper Triassic (Keuper). Locality: Württemberg, Germany. Length of the frond:
20 cm. (7.8 inches)

The extensive sea of Muschelkalk time retreated once more, and the
alluvial plains of the Keuper followed. Occasionally the showy fronds
of plants related to the cycads are found in the sandstones of the south
German middle Keuper. The trunks of these plants are unkown; they
must have stood outside the area of deposition of the sandstone. A related
Recent plant is *Cycas revoluta,* used as a funereal decorative plant, whose
habitat is in Asia. Together with the conifers, the cycads were the dominant types of higher plants during millions of years, from the Upper
Permian to the Lower Cretaceous.

PAGE **61**   DINOSAUR SKULL *(Plateosaurus)*
Upper Triassic (Keuper). Locality: Trossingen, Württemberg, Germany. Length
of the skull: about 30 cm. (11.7 inches). Total length of the animal: 5.75 meters
(18.8 feet)

The Keuper is characterized by repeated alternations of clay and sandy
deposits. During a period of drought in the middle Keuper, the dinosaurs
("giant lizards") of the land gathered at muddy water holes to drink.
One of these gathering places has been found in the vicinity of the
present-day town of Trossingen. Many of these animals must have
become trapped in the mud and died there, for the bones of several
dozen of these dinosaurs have been unearthed by excavations under-
taken at this locality. The lightweight skull is pierced by numerous
foramina ("windows"), a condition that points to a common origin
with the pterosaurs ("winged lizards") and the birds. The dentition,
consisting of a large number of undifferentiated teeth, suggests that the
food of this saurian comprised all sorts of small animals. The propor-
tions of the front and hind legs are similar to those of the kangaroo,

and in rapid running the plateosaur may have used only the hind legs. Our Keuper dinosaurs represent the ancestral forms of the gigantosaurs, which have been found in Jurassic and Cretaceous deposits in North America and eastern Africa.

PAGE **63** SKULL OF A FOSSIL GIANT TURTLE *(Proganochelys)*

Upper Triassic (Keuper). Locality: Aixheim, near Trossingen, Württemberg, Germany. Length of the skull: 12 cm. (4.7 inches)

From a bed of Keuper sandstone, skull and carapace of a land turtle were recovered as a result of a fortunate chance discovery. The carapace measures 70 cm. (27.3 inches) in length; the entire animal may have been more than a meter (39.4 inches) long. The skull, in contrast to that of *Plateosaurus,* forms a closed capsule, in which the large eye sockets, bordered by protruding bony plates, are sunk. Upon the toothless jaws there was probably, instead, a horny beak, as in present-day turtles, and the food, therefore, may also have been similar. The origin of the turtles must lie even farther back in geologic time, for by Keuper time they already appeared in various forms.

PAGE **65** SUTURE PATTERN OF AN AMMONITE CEPHALOPOD

(Arcestes)

Upper Triassic of the Alps. Locality: Hallstatt, Upper Austria. Diameter 8 cm. (3.1 inches)

While the Bunter sandstone, Muschelkalk and Keuper were being deposited in the German Graben, the open sea of the Triassic spread over the south. In it, a profuse development of marine animals took place, which is remarkable especially for the extraordinary multiplicity of form in the ammonites, and the evolution of their suture patterns. In our *Arcestes* the outer shell material has been carefully polished in order to show the beautiful lace pattern of the suture lines (see the explanation of page 57). The course of the septa becomes simpler toward the interior of the shell, as the more deeply cut section in the lower right shows.

PAGE **67** RETICULATE FERN *(Dictyophyllum acutilobum)*

Upper Triassic (Rhaetic sandstone of the uppermost Keuper). Locality: Nürtingen, Württemberg, Germany. Length of the leaf: 7.5 cm. (2.9 inches)

The waves of the sea inundated the treeless plains and swamplands of what had previously been dry land; premonitory signs of the Jurassic sea are seen, and over wide areas we find its near-shore deposits. The Rhaetic sandstone was formed in this way, with its marine pelecypod shells, but also with drifted remains of land plants. Nothing is left of the leaf substance of our reticulated fern in the sandstone, which is permeable by moisture, yet the form and the venation are clearly visible in the impression, and stand out because of a thin natural coating of limonite. The specimen looks like the leaf of a tree, but it is a fern, which here, with its venation, is already anticipating a structure possessed by later higher plants. Relatives of *Dictyophyllum* still grow today, but only in tropical Asia.

PAGE **69** AN AMMONITE OF THE JURASSIC SEA *(Amaltheus solaris)*
Lower Jurassic (Lias). Locality: Reichenbach, near Aalen, Württemberg, Germany. Diameter of the ammonite: 3 cm. (1.2 inches)

The ammonite shell, with its beautiful crescentically curved costae and ornamental keel, rests on a sparkling golden mass of pyrite crystals. Sulfuric acid from decaying animal bodies combined with dissolved iron from the dark sea mud to form iron sulfide, or pyrite, which is here solidified, together with the ammonite, in the form of a massive precipitate. The various species of ammonites often combined a short span of existence with wide geographic distribution, and are therefore among the most valuable guide fossils, which are used in identifying rock formations of the same ages.

PAGE **71** JURASSIC CYPRESS *(Cupressites liasinus)*
Lower Jurassic (Lias). Locality: Holzmaden, Württemberg, Germany. Length of the branch: 21 cm. (8.2 inches)

Leaves and branches of plants are rare in the shales of the southern German upper Lias. Storms on the mainland may have broken off parts of the plants, and marine currents may have carried them away, but the coast lay far away from the localities where we find them now. Only a few specimens of *Cupressites liasinus* are known; a particularly beautiful branch, preserved in carbonaceous material, lies here in the shale. The plant undoubtedly belongs to the true conifers; it has not been possible, however, to determine the relationship more precisely, in spite of microscopic study of the cell structure of the leaves. The remains of a second conifer, similar to the Recent Araucarias, are found somewhat more commonly, as well as fronds of various cycadaceous plants. As early as the Upper Permian, the plant kingdom, with the conifers, began its advance upon the land, which previously, during the age of the moisture-requiring fern-like plants, must have been still entirely free of larger plant life. The conifers and related forms then maintained their dominance until the appearance of the flowering plants in the Upper Cretaceous.

PAGE **73** BIRTH OF AN ICHTHYOSAUR *(Ichthyosaurus quadriscissus)*
Lower Jurassic (Lias). Locality: Holzmaden, Württemberg, Germany. Length of the newborn individual: 55 cm. (21.5 inches)

A process of birth about 150 million years old! The posterior part of the head, with the large protective plates for the eyes, the body, and the tail of the young individual are free, but a pelvic bone of the adult animal

13

lies across the snout of the young. Between the ribs of the adult ichthyosaur, the disarticulated vertebrae of more young can be seen. The vertebral column of the adult animal runs across the upper part of the plate. It appears quite obvious that the ichthyosaurs brought their young into the world alive, in the sea, for one can hardly imagine how these animals, which passed their lives so completely in the water, could have emerged on dry land to lay their eggs. Here a mother animal, very possibly at the point of death, expelled the young individual, which was ready for birth, and the mud of the sea bottom spread its gray shroud over both of them.

PAGE **75**   ARMORED CROCODILE *(Mystriosaurus)*

Lower Jurassic (upper Lias). Locality: Holzmaden, Württemberg, Germany. Length of the skeleton: 185 cm. (72 inches)

A prepared specimen from the workshop of Dr. Hauff in Holzmaden. The bony mass, indurated by the infiltration of calcium carbonate, is harder than the shale, and can therefore be cleared of matrix in completely life-like form. In contrast to the smooth-skinned *Ichthyosaurus*, we see here both dorsal and ventral armor, which are preserved in exceptionally complete form. The dwarfed forelegs suggest that their function was, at most, only to control direction in swimming. Could the break in the skull have been the cause of death? The loop in the tail may have been added after the death of the animal, as a result of a trick of the waves. The bottom of an isolated part of the sea, where no scavengers lived, saturated with toxic matter, preserved this splendid witness to the events of the past.

PAGE **77**   CROSS SECTION OF AN AMMONITE SHELL *(Ludwigia)*

Middle Jurassic (lower Dogger). Locality: Wasseralfingen, Württemberg, Germany. Diameter 23 cm. (9 inches)

An ammonite has been sectioned in the median plane to show the chambers in the interior of the shell. This subdivision of the shell into air chambers for swimming marks the ammonite as a relative of the *Nautilus* that still lives today in the Indian Ocean. It clearly differentiates the ammonites, on the other hand, from the snails, whose shells are never chambered. The apertural end of the shell, with the living chamber for the ammonite animal, is broken away in our prepared specimen, and the septa of the "air chambers" follow a very simple course here in the median plane of the shell. The crenulation of the septa that is so characteristic of the fossil ammonites occurs only as they approach the outer wall of the shell. During burial on the sea bottom, mud was washed into only a few of the closed chambers. Most of them are lined with beautiful crystal growths, the substance of which came from stagnating mineral solutions in the chamber cavities.

14

CRATICULARIA ("Gridiron Sponge"), a marine sponge
(Craticularia)

*Upper Jurassic (middle Malm). Locality: Swabian Alps, Germany. Height of
the fossil: 7 cm. (2.7 inches)*

The sponges are among the most simply organized of animal life. Their
food, composed of very small organic particles, is swirled in through
numerous openings in the outer wall, and the waste is ejected upward
through a larger opening that runs through the center of the sponge.
A well-known example is the bath sponge, which, however, in itself
represents a colony of such sponges. Whereas the skeleton of the bath
sponge consists of a perishable mass of horn (chitin), in the sponges
preserved as fossils it is constructed of very fine siliceous or calcareous
spicules. Siliceous and calcareous sponges still live in present-day seas.
The "gridiron sponge" shown in the plate is a siliceous sponge. It was
covered over by calcareous mud collecting on the sea bottom, and finally
deposits of calcite also replaced the siliceous substance of the skeleton.
It is now composed entirely of calcite. The latticework of its wall has
been coarsened by the natural effects of weathering. The Jurassic rocks
of the Swabian and Franconian Alps contain these siliceous sponges in
great abundance, and their multiplicity of forms still increased in the
Cretaceous.

KNIFE CORAL *(Thecosmilia trichotoma)*

*Upper Jurassic (Malm). Nattheim, near Heidenheim, Württemberg, Germany.
Height: 6 cm. (2.3 inches)*

While the siliceous skeletons of the sponges in the Jurassic rocks are
mostly replaced by calcite, the originally calcareous skeletons of the
corals in the upper beds of the Malm are frequently replaced by siliceous
material. From the sometimes weaker, sometimes stronger degree of
silicification, we can conclude that this was a subsequent process that
took place in the rock. The fact that the coral skeletons are preserved
in silica now makes it possible for us to free the calices from their
calcareous matrix by careful etching with dilute hydrochloric acid, and
to dissolve them out in all their knife-sharp detail.

"TURBAN" SEA-URCHIN *(Cidaris coronata)*

*Upper Jurassic (upper Malm). Locality: Sontheim, near Heidenheim on the
Brenz River, Württemberg, Germany. Width of the test: 5.5 cm. (2.1 inches)*

After the death of the animal, the organic ligamentous matter that
covered it and held the long spines on the articular tubercles of the
test decomposed; the spines fell off and were washed away. The sea
urchin minus its spines has now become a true show piece. Each of the
articular tubercles is situated upon a separate pedestal (once in a way
two are seen to occur together), and the latter are linked together in
double rows. Longitudinal furrows and narrow lines of pores separate

the bands of spines from each other. Through the closely set fine pores, the "feet" of the sea urchin once protruded; they were connected with a pumping mechanism located in the interior of the test. The "feet" served primarily for the intake of oxygen. In locomotion, the present-day *Cidaris* uses its long spines, with which it walks about on the sea-bottom as if on stilts. The test now lies with the oral aperture upward; the living sea urchin, however, is oriented with its oral aperture down, toward the sea bottom. The test, originally composed of calcium carbonate, has been subsequently silicified, and it was therefore possible to etch it so completely out of the rock.

PAGE **85** DRAGONFLY *(Petalia longialata)*

Upper Jurassic (Malm). Locality: Eichstätt, Bavaria, southeastern Germany. Length of the animal: 16 cm. (6.3 inches)

A delicate dragonfly, which lived many millions of years ago, is here preserved so distinctly in the rock that even the venation of the wings can be studied in detail. Wind and water may have carried the animal from the mainland and deposited it upon the mud of the shore, where it was embedded, together with other insects, land animals and plant remains. As early as the Carboniferous, primitive insects belonging to various groups occur, among which is a "primitive dragonfly," whose wing span has been reported as 70 cm. (27.3 inches).

PAGE **87** GANOID (Enamel-scaled Fish) *(Gyrodus hexagonus)*

Upper Jurassic (Malm). Locality: Solnhofen, Bavaria, Germany. Height of the fish: 22 cm. (8.6 inches)

The ganoids accompany the placoderms (armored fish) in the Paleozoic, and are transitional to the subsequently dominant bony fishes (teleosts) in the Mesozoic. They represent the principal group of fishes in the later Paleozoic and in the Mesozoic. Their vertebral column is cartilaginous, but the body bears an armor of rigid enamel scales. Each of these scales consists of a bony plate which is overlaid with a hard, shining layer of enamel similar to that of our teeth. The disciform, almost hexagonal ganoid fish shown in the plate was provided with a specialized set of broad grinding teeth, with which it could crush small marine shellfish. It probably moved around slowly, swimming near the bottom, with its large eyes on the lookout for prey.

PAGE **89** PRIMITIVE BIRD *(Archaeornis siemensi)*

Upper Jurassic (upper Malm). Locality: Vicinity of Eichstätt, Bavaria, Germany. Size of the slab: about 40 × 50 cm. (5.6 × 9.5 inches)

When we look at the fossil slab, we notice first the half-spread wing feathers. They are attached to the angularly bent forelegs (or arms), each of which is still provided with three free claw-bearing digits. The neck and head lie bent backward. The large eye socket is easily visible, but the dentition present in the jaws is scarcely recognizable in the photograph. The two hind legs are articulated to the pelvis. The shanks and the long tail are bilaterally feathered. This primitive bird may have once been washed up as a carcass on the mud flats of a calm embayment of the sea. Its habitat, however, was a thinly forested area; there it moved about in gliding flight from tree to tree, and used its clawed toes to hold fast to the branches. *Archaeornis*, and likewise the closely related *Archaeopteryx*, are counted among the most remarkable creatures that ever lived, because they combine the characteristics of reptiles with the feathers of birds. They show that the avian feather was already invented by the end of Jurassic time. In the following Cretaceous period, the shortened tail was added, and by the beginning of the Tertiary, the dentition of the jaws had also disappeared in the birds.

PAGE **91** MARINE CRAYFISH *(Meyeria rapax)*

Lower Cretaceous. Locality: Sachsenhagen, Schaumburg-Lippe, Germany.
Width of the concretion: about 20 cm. (7.8 inches)

This crayfish lies embedded in a hard calcareous concretion, which has protected it from being completely crushed. It belongs to the division of crustaceans called *Decapoda*, to which our well-known Recent marine and fresh-water crayfish, lobster and crab belong. The union of the cephalon and thorax in a cephalothoracic carapace is characteristic of all of them. The segments of the abdomen are attached to the cephalothoracic carapace of the fossil, which is covered with a fine, pustulate granulation. The tail end is bent downward in a remarkable manner, and may have enabled the animal to make swimming strokes for purposes of locomotion. Nevertheless, *Meyeria* was not a true swimming crustacean; the animal must rather have progressed by crawling on the sea bottom with its locomotor appendages. Below the cephalothoracic carapace, the stoutly constructed anterior pair of appendages is recognizable.

PAGE **93** LEAF OF A TREE *(Credneria)*

Upper Cretaceous. Locality: Blankenburg, Harz Mountains, Germany.
Natural size

In the later part of Cretaceous time, a significant change took place in the plant kingdom. The flowering plants became the dominant element in the vegetational covering of the earth. *Credneria* is shown here as an example. Only the leaf, preserved as an impression in sandstone, is known. This is an extinct plant species, apparently a relative of the plane trees. With the appearance of these flowering plants, the insects took on their allotted role as transmitters of pollen, and the nutritional basis was provided for the vast development of the birds and mammals that followed in Tertiary time.

PAGE **95** HELICALLY COILED AMMONITE *(Bostrichoceras polyplocum)*

Upper Cretaceous. Locality: Haldem, Westphalia, Germany. Height: 9 cm. (3.5 inches)

The ammonites of the Triassic and Jurassic almost without exception maintained a closed spiral type of coiling and a completely bilaterally symmetrical shell form. In the Cretaceous, however, many of these animals show a remarkable disturbance of form. The spire opens out to boat-shaped (scaphoid) and hook-shaped (uncinate) shapes, and even to the form of a straight staff (bacilliform). The convolutions of the shell tend to leave the plane of coiling and to take on the form of a helix or corkscrew curl. One might say that this was the "baroque period" of the ammonites. At the end of the Cretaceous, they became extinct. The helical ammonite shown in the plate could probably live only near the sea bottom; it is hardly possible to suppose that an animal with a shell of this type was an active swimmer.

PAGE **97** RUDISTID PELECYPOD *(Hippurites radiosus)*

("Striated Horsetail Mussel")

Upper Cretaceous. Locality: Charente, southern France. Width of the colony: 35 cm. (13.6 inches)

The hippurites are an example of how much the manner of living can influence the form. The valve attached to the bottom became a calyx, in which the animal progressed upward by constructing transverse septa. The opposing valve, on the other hand, consisted of only a flat cover. Several calices might also grow together to form a colony, probably in order to steady themselves in the surf. The hippurites thus took on an external appearance similar to that of the corals, and for a long time were not recognized as pelecypods. It is probable that a warm climate was a necessity for their growth. The restriction of their reef-like colonies to certain areas has contributed to the assumption of climatic zones during Cretaceous time.

PAGE **99** TELEOST (Bony fish) *(Priscacara pealei)*

Older Tertiary. Locality: Green River, Wyoming. Length of the fish: 12 cm. (4.7 inches)

The great change in the fishes took place as early as the Cretaceous. The armor-clad ganoids with cartilaginous skeletons receded, and the teleosts, with bony internal skeleton and a thin external covering of scales, became dominant. Greater mobility was attained in this way, which must have given the animal an advantage not only in the pursuit of its prey, but also in escaping from its enemies. In the fossil, the bony vertebral column is recognizable behind the head with its wide-open mouth. The dorsal fin above, with the structure of the anterior portion different from that of the posterior, recalls the perch. Anteriorly, the strong "hard" rays can be seen; behind them follow the brush-like "soft" rays. The same condition is found in the fins of the ventral side. All the more important groups of teleosts living today were already represented in the Tertiary.

PAGE **101** SKULL OF A "PRIMITIVE HORSE" *(Palaeotherium crassum)*
Older Tertiary. Locality: Gypsum bed at Montmartre, near Paris. Length of the skull: about 27 cm. (10.5 inches)

By the end of the Triassic, reptiles had, in some of their characteristics, approached the condition of mammals. Thereafter, from the Jurassic and Cretaceous, a number of small mammals are known. But with the beginning of the Cenozoic era, they experienced a positively explosive outburst in their development. The age of mammals replaced the age of reptiles. *Palaeotherium* is an especially important genus of the older Tertiary. The most famous finds are those studied by Cuvier, from the gypsum beds of Montmartre, near Paris, which were deposited in residual basins of a retreating sea. The skull shows a sinus that extends unusually far back below the nasal bone, and a tapir-like proboscis structure was formerly postulated in reconstructing the Palaeotherium. The fore and hind feet of this ancient perissodactyl were three-toed. The Palaeotheria are a side line that soon became extinct, in the evolution of the horse, the end member of which is the single-toed horse.

PAGE **103** "PEARLY TURRET SHELL" *(Cerithium margaritatum)*, a snail
Early Tertiary. Locality: Weinheim, Mainz Basin, Germany. Size of the slab: 12 × 17 cm. (4.7 × 6.7 inches)

Subsidence processes, which began during older Tertiary time in the upper Rhine region and progressed gradually until they involved even the more northerly-lying parts of the Rhineland, resulted in an invasion of the sea from neighboring ocean basins. Thus there came about the precipitation of the potash beds of Alsace and southern Baden, and the deposition of marine sands in the Mainz Basin and adjacent areas. Emergence of the land interrupted the connections between the seas. Fresh water became mixed with the land-locked salt water. In this brackish water, with its low salt content, *Cerithium* and related snails, as well as the pelecypod *Cyrena* (center of the slab shown in the plate), seem to have found favorable conditions for their life, for their accumulated shells fill many beds of the rock in great numbers.

PAGE **105** LEAF OF A FAN PALM *(Sabal major)*
Middle Tertiary. Locality: Münzenberg, Hessen, Germany. Length of the leaf fragment: 26 cm. (10.2 inches)

We recognize the distinctive fanlike folding of the palm leaf; a deeply notched marginal area, such as the leaves of Recent fan palms exhibit, is not preserved here, however. In the dense Münzenberg sandstone, the

19

fossil shows carbonaceous material in places. Palms are today indicative of tropical and subtropical regions. We must assume that a tropical climate also predominated in central Europe in early Tertiary time, and that its retreat, first from central Germany and then from southern Germany, was accompanied by the gradual disappearance of palm trees.

PAGE **107**   MAPLE LEAF *(Acer)*

Middle Tertiary. Locality: Bohling Gorge on the Schnierenberg, Baden, Germany. Width of the leaf: 15 cm. (5.9 inches)

The sea, which had reached the southern margin of the Swabian Alps, finally retreated during the course of the middle Tertiary. In the broad fresh-water basins that remained after its retreat, sand, clay, and limy mud were deposited, and the foliage of the surrounding plant growth was interbedded with them by the wind. This vast "fossil herbarium" yielded numerous plant forms in the past, from the quarries near Öhningen at the lower end of Lake Constance; some of them are related to present-day North American species, and some to those of the Mediterranean region and the Orient. The climate at that time was probably similar to that of the present-day Mediterranean countries. In more recent times, excavations carried on by the Geological Institute of Freiburg University in nearby Bohling Gorge have brought to light a rich new treasure trove of the same plant assemblage, from which the leaf shown in our plate was taken.

PAGE **109**   FORK-HORNED DEER *(Heteroprox larteti)*

Middle Tertiary. Locality: Steinheim on the Albuch, Württemberg, Germany. Length of the skull: about 20 cm. (7.8 inches)

The skull lay in the soft Steinheim gastropod-marl. Thus the thin-boned anterior portion was crushed by the pressure of the rock, but the rows of hard teeth and the roof of the skull with the antlers are well preserved. In general, only these harder parts of the skull can be recovered by excavating in the sand. The antlers of this Tertiary deer are unusual in the length of the burr stocks, which are implanted directly over the orbits, and in the lack of a true burr; in addition, the male possesses an ensiform canine tooth in the upper jaw. In the older Tertiary, the formation of antlers in the deer is altogether unknown, and nothing approaching the stately present-day antlers occurs before the late Tertiary. Fork-horned deer, antlerless large deer, a three-toed primitive horse, rhinoceros, Tertiary elephants, and many other animals came to drink at that time to the lake in the Steinheim Basin. Many of them were mangled by predatory animals, and remains of the dead animals came to be embedded in the limy mud of the lake. Surely these same animals also lived at that time in the countryside all around, but their bones could be preserved for us only in a place that was favorable.

"MUMMIFIED" SPIDER *(Aviculariidae?)*

Middle Tertiary. Locality: Böttingen, near Münsingen, Swabian Alps, Germany. Length of the fossil: 4.5 cm. (1.75 inches)

The earlier and middle Tertiary were times of particular unrest in the earth's crust. The Alps and other mountain ranges were then being compressed into folds by a vast thrusting process. In the region of the Swabian Alps, the subterranean pressure was relieved in many places by the extrusion of lava flows. The locality Böttingen, near Münsingen, is situated upon one of these places where extrusion took place. But during the middle Tertiary, the plug that filled the eruption chimney, composed of volcanic debris, sank back again, so that a wide fissure developed at its edge, next to the surrounding Jurassic rocks. Carbonate-bearing mineral hot springs then arose in this fissure. Fallen leaves and animals of the vicinity, which accidentally fell into the fissure, were coated by the rapidly precipitating calcareous sinter. This is what happened to this spider, which struggled in vain to climb out; it is preserved now, as the broken-off places show, only as an empty hollow.

MOLAR TOOTH OF AN ANCIENT MAMMOTH
(Elephas trogontherii)

Pleistocene. Locality: Süssenborn, near Weimar, Thuringia, Germany. Size of the specimen: 9 × 11 cm. (3.5 × 4.3 inches)

After the Tertiary, for which a duration of about 60 million years is estimated, there follows, as the last epoch of earth history, the Quaternary (= Pleistocene plus Holocene, or Recent), with a disproportionately short duration of one-half to one million years. Of this time, 10,000 years are allowed for the Recent, the present day of earth history. Among the most remarkable animals of the Pleistocene, or Ice Age, is the mammoth. The penultimate molar tooth from the left lower jaw of a primitive mammoth, an ancestral form restricted to the older Pleistocene, is illustrated here. We are looking at the grinding surfaces of the tooth, which had already been strongly worn down (four of them are already gone), and we notice, at the lower left end, a strong indentation resulting from contact with the last molar, which followed it posteriorly and moved up to replace it. The elephant possesses only one molar in each half of each jaw, plus, at most, a portion of the next following molar, simultaneously available for chewing. This restriction in the number of simultaneously functional teeth is compensated for by the enlargement of the grinding surfaces and the nature of their structure. Numerous consecutively arranged links of hard, fluted enamel, which surround the softer dentine, and a connective tooth cement that is also soft, serve to maintain the grinding surface always rough and suitable for grinding up the food, which consists of plants.

21

PAGE **115** OAK LEAVES *(Quercus)*

Pleistocene. Locality: Bad Cannstatt, Württemberg, Germany.
Size of the specimen: 9 × 11 cm. (3.5 × 4.3 inches)

During a warmer period of the later Pleistocene, in the vicinity of Bad
Cannstatt, leaves, fruit, twigs and even whole tree trunks were coated
and impregnated with the yellow-brown travertine that was precipitated
from the carbonate-bearing springs, which at that time flowed more
copiously. They are, in all cases, the plants that also grow today in the
area. In contrast to this situation, the contemporaneous animal assemblage is characterized by forms that have since become extinct, such as
the forest elephant, a Pleistocene rhinoceros, cave bears, and others.

PAGE **117** "PETRIFIED BRAIN" OF A CAVE BEAR *(Ursus spelaeus)*

Pleistocene. Locality: Bad Cannstatt, Württemberg, Germany.
Length of the specimen: 13 cm. (5.1 inches)

Only the middle portion of the brain is preserved; the anterior and
posterior parts are lacking. In the upper right, a fragment of the skull
wall is still present in the rock. The convolutions and furrows of the
brain surface are clearly visible, as well as the blood vessels, even in
their finer ramifications. The stout longitudinal cord in the center
represents the venous "longitudinal blood vessel," which is embedded
in a furrow running along the inner side of the roof of the skull. Travertine, precipitated by carbonate-bearing mineral water, has partly filled
the brain cavity of a cave bear's skull that came by chance into the
area of the springs. By breaking the stone and chipping away the surrounding bony wall, the distinct mold of the interior was brought to
light, which now reproduces the form of the brain surface.

PAGE **119** IVORY CARVING (Lioness?)

Younger Old Stone Age of the Pleistocene. Locality: Stetten Cave, Swabian
Alps, Germany. Length of the carving: 9 cm. (3.5 inches)

Rocks tell us not only of advances and retreats of the sea, of the building
of mountain ranges, and of plants and animals; they also tell us of
human beings from an earlier age. The sand of Pleistocene rivers, and
travertine deposits and cave fillings of the Pleistocene, bring us knowledge of primitive men. In a cave near Stetten above Lontal in the
Swabian Alps, small figures of animals have been excavated, which
represent the mammoth, the aurochs, the wild horse, the reindeer, and
possibly the cave lion; they were lying associated with actual remains
of these animals and with the skull of a man. The "Homo sapiens fos-
silis" worked these carvings out of mammoth ivory, and put magic
symbols on them, probably in order to hold the animals, upon which
his life depended, in his power.

LIST OF PLATES

All photographs are of specimens in the collections of the Staatliches Museum für Naturkunde (State Museum of Natural History) in Stuttgart. Six of the pictures were taken from casts. Some of the originals of these casts are also in the Stuttgart Museum (pages 61, 63, 73), others are in the Museum of Natural History in Berlin (page 89), in the Museum of Natural History in Paris (page 101), and in the Institute of Prehistory of the University of Tübingen (page 119).

TRILOBITES ("THREE-LOBED ANIMALS")

Ellipsocephalus hoffi

Middle Cambrian

SHED CARAPACES OF TRILOBITES

Dalmanitina socialis

Ordovician

27

EURYPTERID ("SPINY-TAILED PADDLE-FOOTED ANIMAL")

Eurypterus lacustris

Silurian

29

UNCOILED NAUTILOID CEPHALOPOD ("STRAIGHT
HORN"), LONGITUDINAL SECTION   *Orthoceras*   31

Silurian

BRACHIOPOD ("ARM-FOOTED ANIMAL")

Spirifer macropterus

Lower Devonian

33

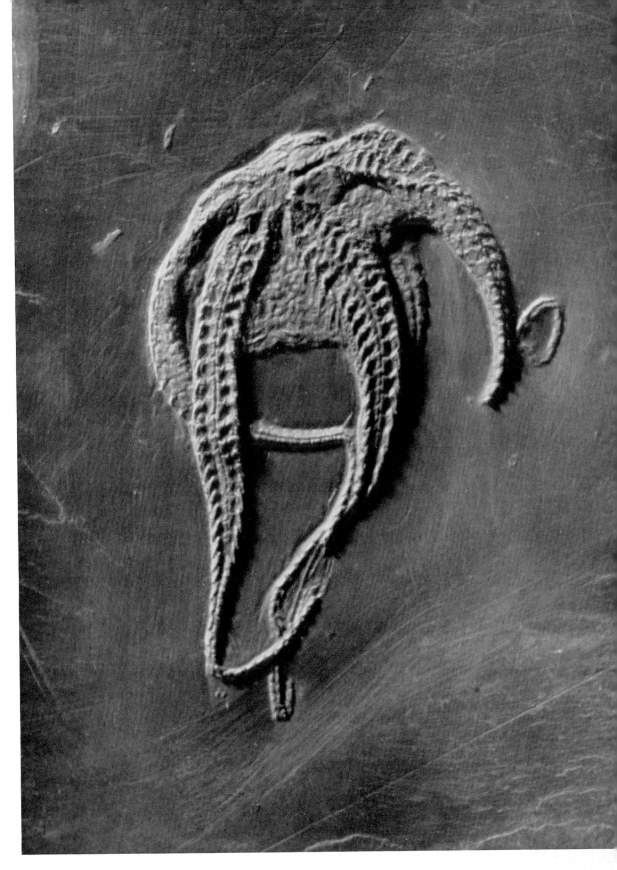

STARFISH (SHIELD-SHAPED SEA-STAR)

Aspidosoma tischbeinianum

Lower Devonian

CRINOID ("SPINY SEA-LILY")

Agriocrinus frechi

Lower Devonian

POLYGONAL CORAL

Cyathophyllum hexagonum

Middle Devonian

PLACODERM (ARMORED FISH)

Bothriolepis canadensis

Upper Devonian

41

"SCALE TREE"

Lepidodendron

Carboniferous

43

"SIGNET TREE," FRAGMENT OF TRUNK

Sigillaria (Favularia)

Carboniferous

FERN

Callipteris conferta

Lower Permian

SKULL OF A STEGOCEPHALIAN (PRIMITIVE AMPHIBIAN)

Archegosaurus decheni

Lower Permian

49

FOOTPRINTS OF A LIZARD-LIKE REPTILE

Chirotherium barthi

Lower Triassic (Bunter sandstone)

AGGLOMERATION OF PELECYPOD SHELLS

Lima striata, Gervilleia socialis

Middle Triassic (Muschelkalk)

THANATOCOENOSIS OF CRINOIDS

Dadocrinus

Middle Triassic (Muschelkalk)

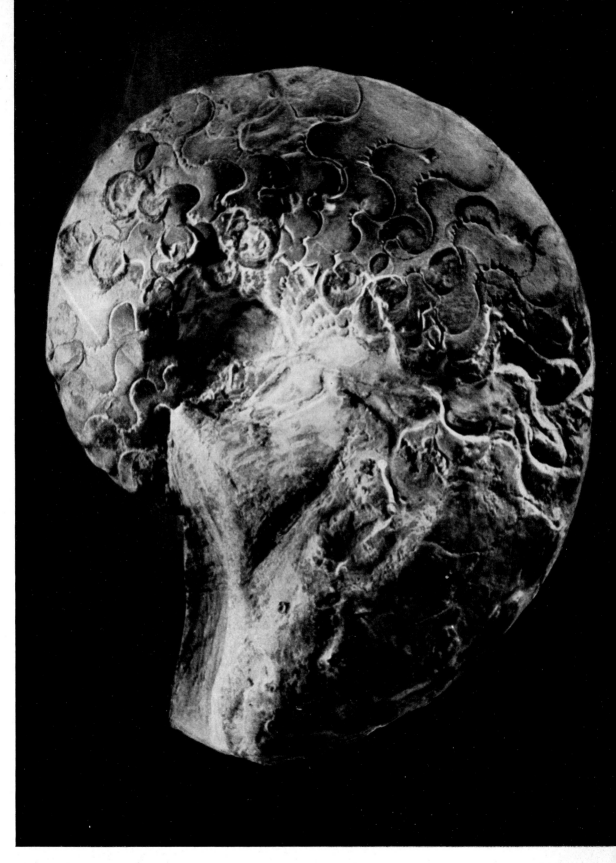

COILED CERATITE CEPHALOPOD ("SERRATED HORN")

Ceratites

Middle Triassic (Muschelkalk)

FROND OF A CYCADACEOUS PLANT

Pterophyllum

Upper Triassic (Keuper)

59

DINOSAUR SKULL

Plateosaurus

Upper Triassic (Keuper)

SKULL OF A FOSSIL GIANT TURTLE

Proganochelys

Upper Triassic (Keuper)

SUTURE PATTERN OF AN AMMONITE CEPHALOPOD

Arcestes

Upper Triassic

RETICULATE FERN

Dictyophyllum acutilobum

Upper Triassic (Keuper)

AN AMMONITE OF THE JURASSIC SEA

Amaltheus solaris

Lower Jurassic (Lias)

BIRTH OF AN ICHTHYOSAUR

Ichthyosaurus quadriscissus

Lower Jurassic (Lias)

ARMORED CROCODILE

Mystriosaurus

Lower Jurassic (Lias)

CROSS SECTION OF AN AMMONITE SHELL

Ludwigia

Middle Jurassic (Dogger)

"GRIDIRON SPONGE"

Craticularia

Upper Jurassic (Malm)

"KNIFE CORAL"

Thecosmilia trichotoma

Upper Jurassic (Malm)

"TURBAN" SEA URCHIN

Cidaris coronata

Upper Jurassic (Malm)

83

DRAGONFLY

Petalia longialata

Upper Jurassic (Malm)

GANOID (ENAMEL-SCALED) FISH

Gyrodus hexagonus

Upper Jurassic (Malm)

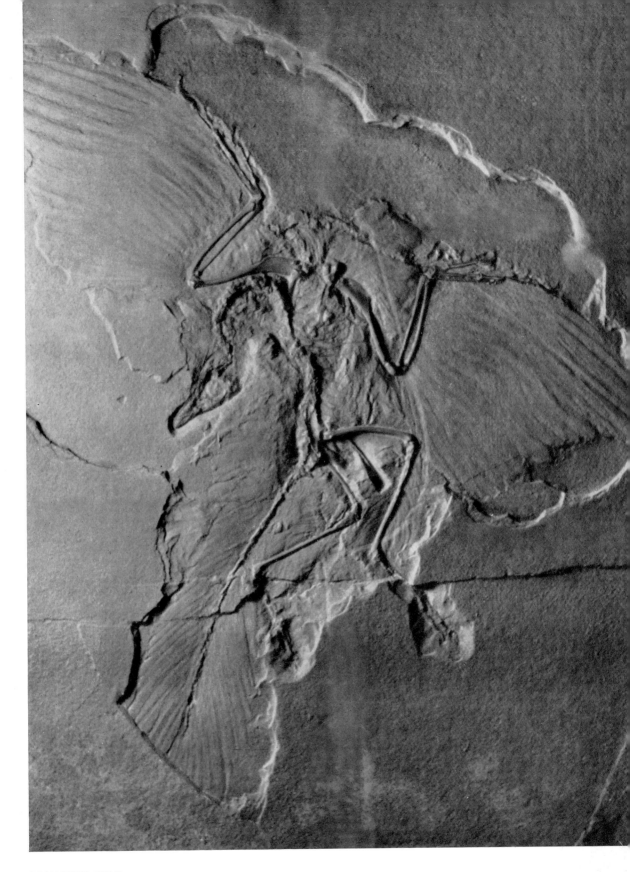

PRIMITIVE BIRD

Archaeornis siemensi

Upper Jurassic (Malm)

MARINE CRAYFISH

Meyeria rapax

Lower Cretaceous

LEAF OF A TREE

Credneria

Upper Cretaceous

HELICALLY COILED AMMONITE

Bostrichoceras polyplocum

Upper Cretaceous

RUDISTID PELECYPOD ("STRIATED HORSE-TAIL MUSSEL")

Hippurites radiosus

Upper Cretaceous

TELEOST (BONY FISH)

Priscacara pealei

Older Tertiary

SKULL OF A "PRIMITIVE HORSE"

Palaeotherium crassum

Older Tertiary

"PEARLY TURRET SHELL"

Cerithium margaritatum

Early Tertiary

LEAF OF A FAN PALM

Sabal major

Middle Tertiary

MAPLE LEAF

Acer

Middle Tertiary

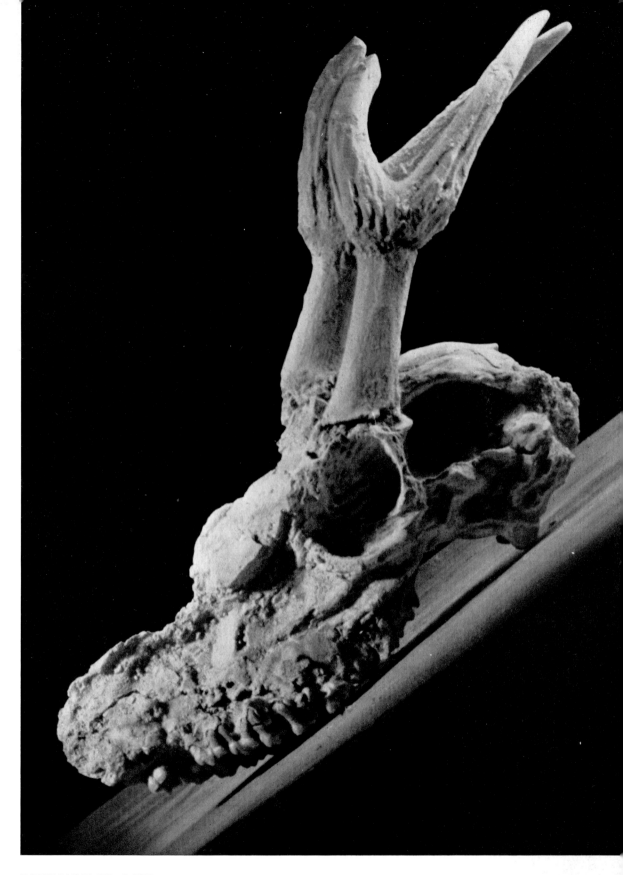

FORK-HORNED DEER

Heteroprox larteti

Middle Tertiary

"MUMMIFIED" SPIDER

Aviculariidae?

Middle Tertiary

MOLAR TOOTH OF AN ANCIENT MAMMOTH

Elephas trogontherii

Older Pleistocene

OAK LEAF

Quercus

Pleistocene

"PETRIFIED BRAIN" OF A CAVE BEAR

Ursus spelaeus

Pleistocene

IVORY CARVING (LIONESS?)

Pleistocene